Copyright © 2021 by Karima Jiwani. Published by J Sisters. PIN & POKE™ All rights reserved. No part of this publication may be reproduced, stored in a retrieval system or transmitted in any form or by any means - electronic, mechanical, photocopying, and recording or otherwise - without prior written permission from the author. The exception would be brief passages by a reviewer in a newspaper or magazine or online. To perform any of the above is an infringement of copyright law.
ISBN: 978-1-7777804-0-1

Images used from Vecteezy.com
Templates and elements are from Canva
Edited by Gray Plume Editorial Services
Content Consultants:
    Nisha Kapoor OCT Certified BE.d Teacher
    Fareen Khimji Registered ECE
    Khodeza Abdulla RECE & Montessori Casa Teacher

THIS BOOK REQUIRES ADULT SUPERVISION
THIS BOOK DOES NOT COME WITH PUSH PIN

WHY ARE PIN POKING OR PUSHPIN SKILLS IMPORTANT?

Poking (or Pushpin) activities are used in the Montessori classroom. It is one of the popular fine motor activities.

Fine Motor Skills are important because they help children complete tasks like writing, feeding oneself, buttoning and zipping.

It also helps to develop:
- Concentration, Focus, Preparation for Writing, Hand–Eye Coordination, Pincer Grip Strength, Patience, Attention to Detail.

INSTRUCTIONS & TIPS

- This book has cut lines. The pages can be cut to be used separately so the other pages are not ruined.

- Dots are wider than traditional poking activities, your child can poke between the dots.

- Items that can be used with this book:
  - Giant Push Pin or Montessori Puncher, Cork Board or Wool Mat (something thick and soft), Tray or Flat Surface and Container or Cup (to hold push pin when not used).

- You can also put construction paper underneath so that your child can copy their work onto the construction paper.

This is book is Level 1 and has Simple lines and Shapes.
For more advanced shapes and designs, please check out:
PIN & POKE™ ~ Fine Motor Skills Activity Book – Level 2

This book is dedicated to two little girls that love to show mommy their pin poking projects.
J Sisters Publishing

PIN & POKE™

FINE MOTOR SKILLS
ACTIVITY BOOK

THIS BOOK BELONGS TO:

....

Let's Make Lines

Let's Make Lines

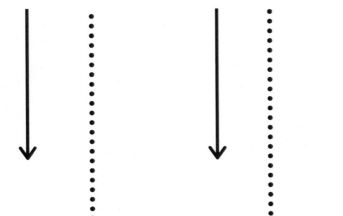
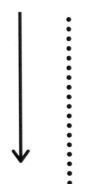

Let's Make Lines

· ·

⟵ —————————

· ·

⟵ —————————

· · · · · · · · · · · · · ·

⟵ —————————

· ·

Let's Make Lines

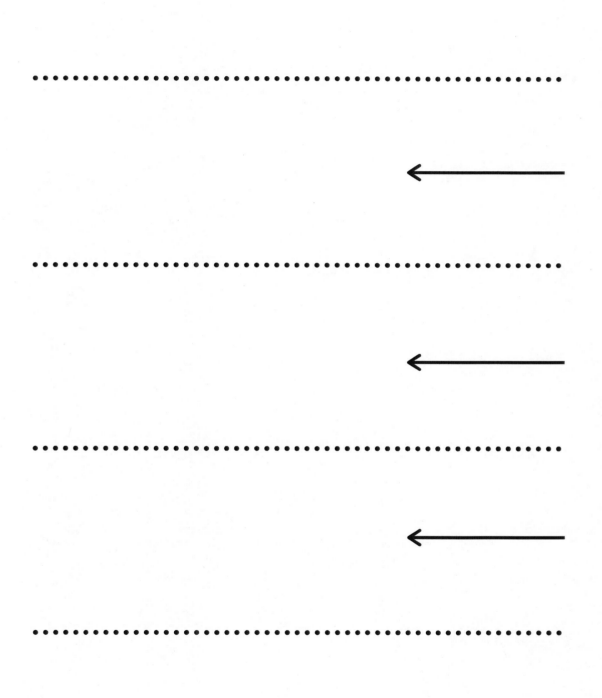

Let's Make Lines

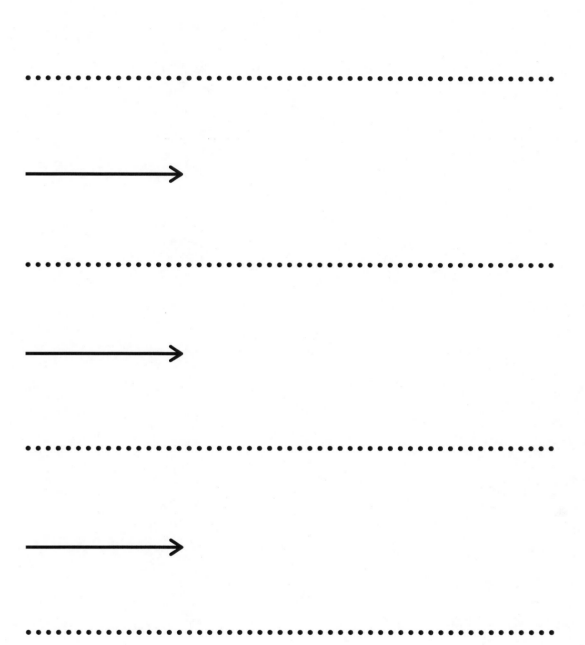

Let's Make Lines

Let's Make an Angle

Let's Make an Angle

Let's Make Angles

Let's Make Angles

Let's Make Angles

Let's Make A Square

Let's Make A Square

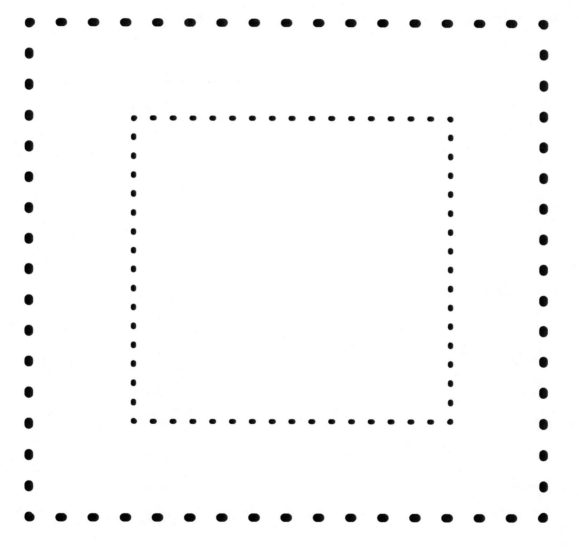

Let's Make Squares

Let's Make A Rectangle

Let's Make Rectangles

Let's Make Lines

Let's Make Lines

Let's Make Lines

Let's Make Lines

Let's Make A Triangle

Let's Make A Triangle

Let's Make Triangles

Let's Make Triangles

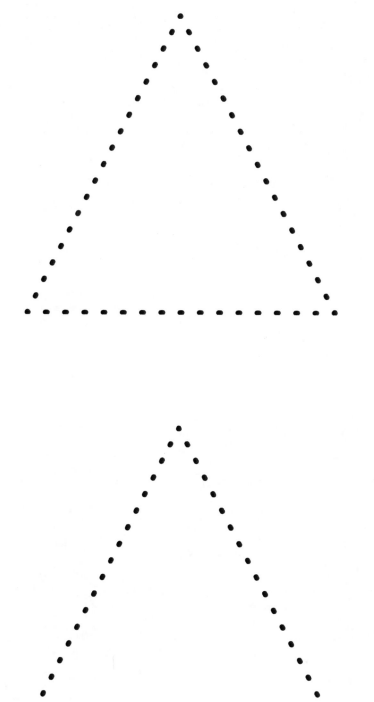

Let's Make A Diamond

Let's Make An Arrow

Let's Make An Arrow

Let's Make A House

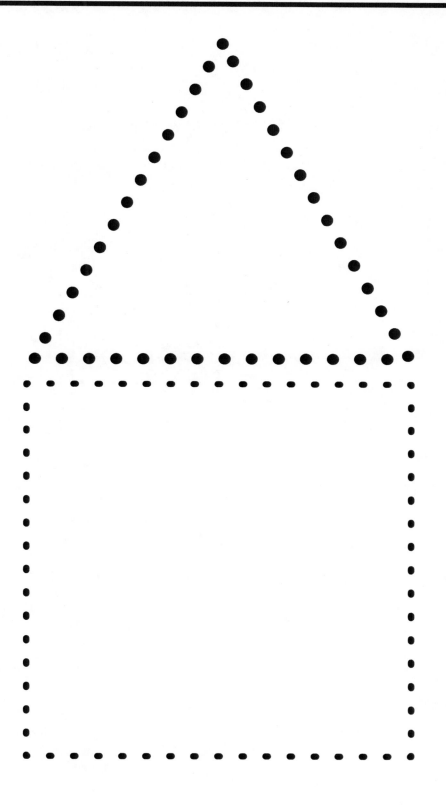

Let's Make A Zig Zag Line

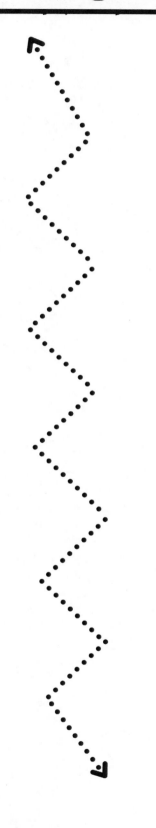

Let's Make Zig Zag Lines

Let's Make Zig Zag Lines

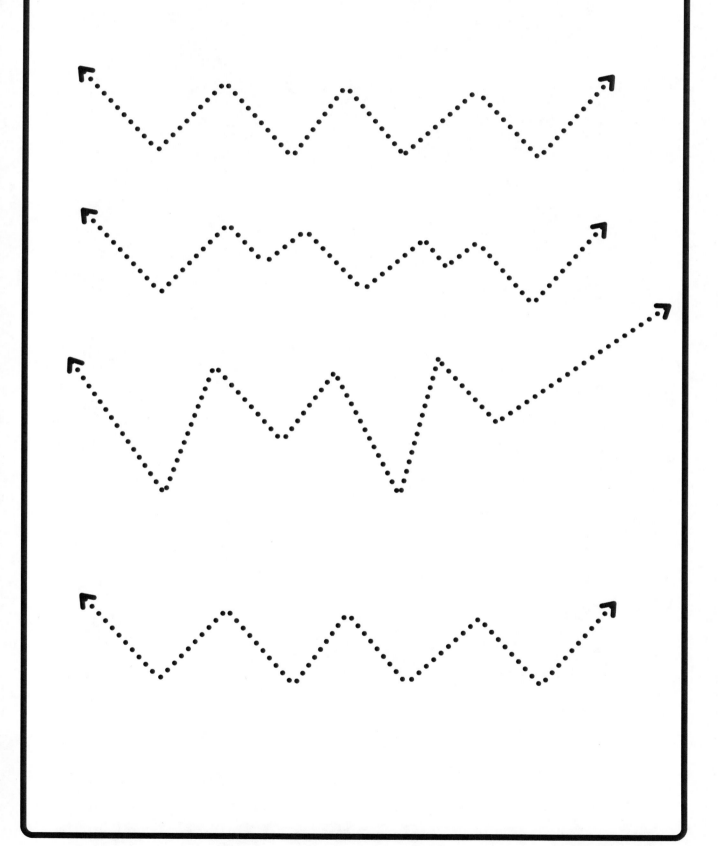

Let's Make A Hexagon

Let's Make A Half Hexagon

Let's Make A Half Hexagon

Let's Make A Hexagon

Let's Make A Star

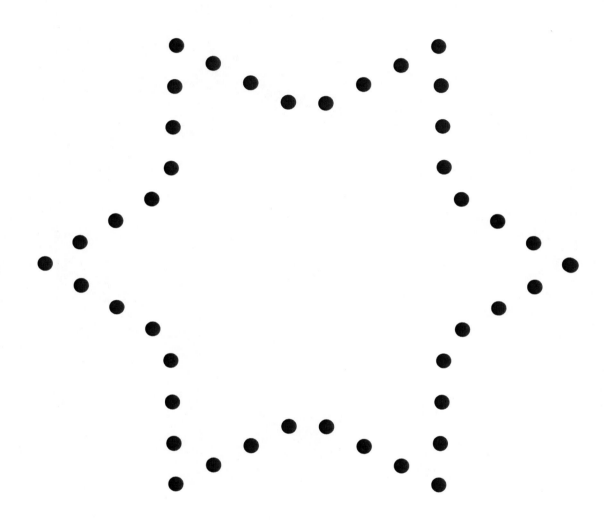

Let's Make A Half Star

Let's Make A Half Star

Let's Make Stars

Let's Make A Curve

Let's Make A Curve

Let's Make A Curve

Let's Make A Curve

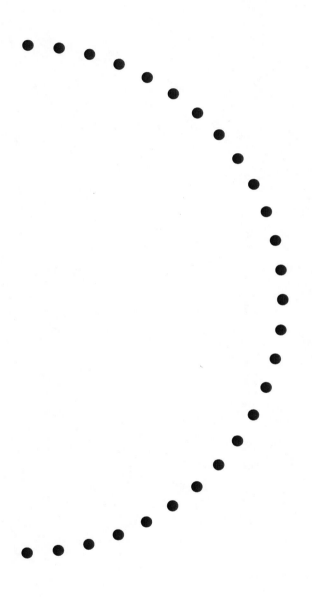

Let's Make A Semicircle

Let's Make A Circle

Let's Make Curves

Let's Make A Curve

Let's Make A Curve

Let's Make A Ring

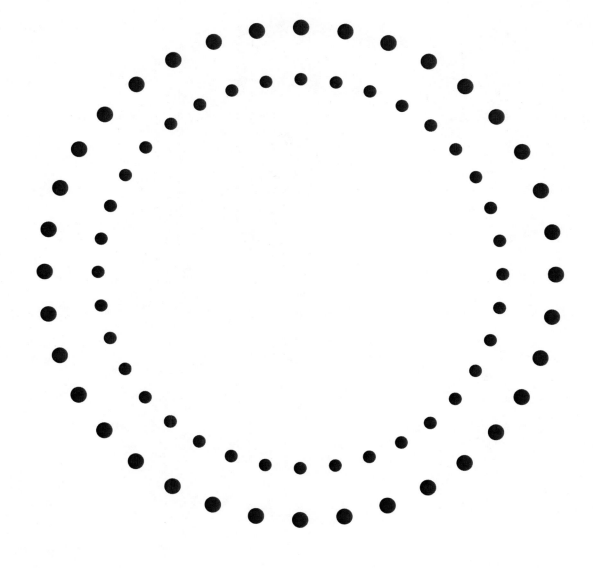

Let's Make Half a Heart

Let's Make Half a Heart

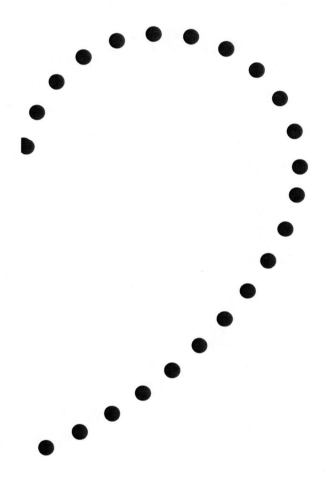

Let's Make A Heart

Let's Make A Flower

Let's Make A Flower

Let's Make Sun Rays

Let's Make The Sun's Face

Let's Make A Sun

◄ •••••••••••••••••••••••••••••• ►

We hope you enjoyed this
PIN & POKE™ Book

For more fun please check out:

PIN & POKE™
Fine Motor Skills Activity Book~ Level 2
on Amazon

Please follow:
 **jsisterspublishing**

Please support us and leave a review.
Thank you

◄ •••••••••••••••••••••••••••••• ►

Made in United States
North Haven, CT
07 February 2023

32160065R00067